The Let
go bo

Near where the Lettermen lived was a large boating lake on which there were all sorts of boats to try out and all sorts of things to go wrong, as we shall see!

First, the Lettermen chose a sailing boat. It wasn't very windy to begin with but the wind got a bit stronger in the middle of the lake. Soon they found the boat much harder to sail than before, especially as the big sail blocked their view of where they were going.

Iso in the middle of the lake was a rowing boat, which some Lettermen had taken out for a quiet little trip. They had all fallen asleep after having their usual enormous breakfast and were not looking where they were going either.

at had bumped into each other
were swimming in the lake.
and everyone was feeling very
nselves.

The Lettermen on the bank who had been w
it was very funny. They were laughing so
hear the motor boat which was coming t

ing all this thought
y that they didn't
ds them very fast...

They got soaked!
There wasn't one
bit of the Lettermen
that wasn't dripping
with water.
Now it was the turn
of the Lettermen in
the water to laugh.

ome others had found a far more peaceful way of enjoying their day out. They'd found an old punt and were gently floating past. One... two... three...

uckily, some canoes were there to help him and soon he was back on dry land.

After all this excitement, the Lettermen realised they hadn't even had time to eat the enormous picnic they'd brought with them. So without any further delay, they set about eating absolutely everything they had in their picnic basket.

When they had finished, they all bought tickets for the big old paddle steamer that took people round the lake every afternoon.

The captain liked t
them steer the sh
middle where they
anything. And you
to hear how the